Ramlal was a cloth merchant. He often sold cloth on credit in nearby villages.

One day, Ramlal was returning from a village after collecting his dues.

He decided to rest for a while under a tree.
Being tired he soon fell asleep.

When Ramlal awoke, he saw a flock of parrots around him.

'How nice it would be if I took one of them home as a pet,' he thought.

Ramlal threw his shoulder scarf on the flock of parrots and caught one.

At his home Ramlal named the parrot 'Totaram.'

He brought a beautiful golden cage for it,
which had a bar, a swing and a bowl.

The parrot was given its favourite food—chillies, guavas and pomegranates.

Ramlal and his children would often talk to the parrot, and the parrot learnt to mimic.

After some time Ramlal again had to go to villages to collect his dues.

He said to Totaram, "I may pass by your old place. Any message for your relatives and friends?"

The parrot answered, "Tell them, in a golden cage I live happily enjoying good food and drinks."

While returning, Ramlal rested again under the same tree.

When he awoke he saw parrots flocking around him.

One of them asked, "Man, where is our friend? How is it?"

"In a golden cage it lives happily enjoying good food and drinks," he repeated the message.

At hearing the message, the parrots dropped themselves down and lay like dead.

Ramlal thought that all the parrots had died of shock.

Upon reaching home, Ramlal said to Totaram, "I repeated your message to your folks and they dropped dead."

At hearing the sad news Totaram too dropped down on the floor of the cage.

Taking his parrot for dead he took it out of the cage sadly and put it under a tree.

Suddenly the parrot flapped its wings and flew up saying, "I got the message of my folks and I go back to them."